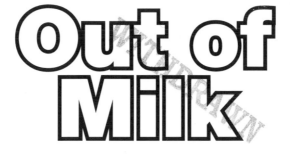

Out of Milk

Written by Alison Hawes

Illustrated by Barbara Vagnozzi

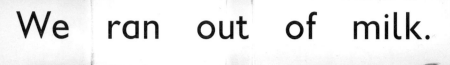

We ran out of milk.

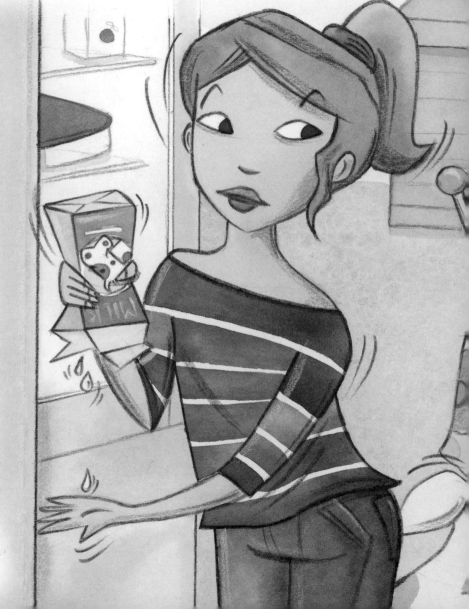

2

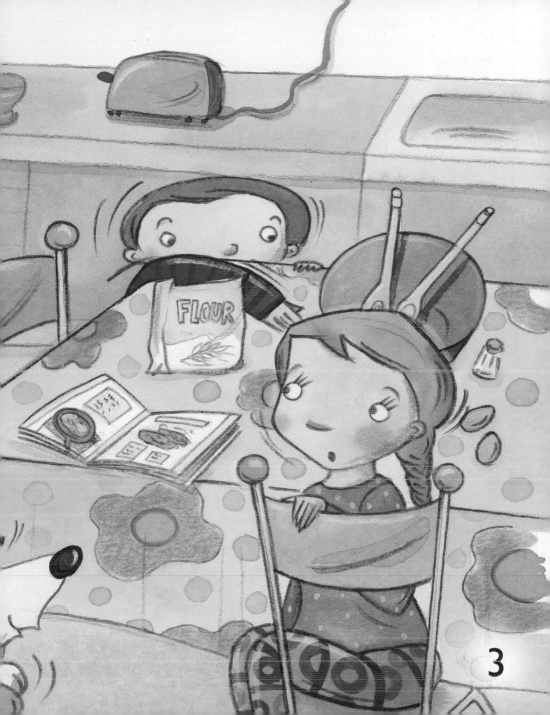

We ran out of the house.

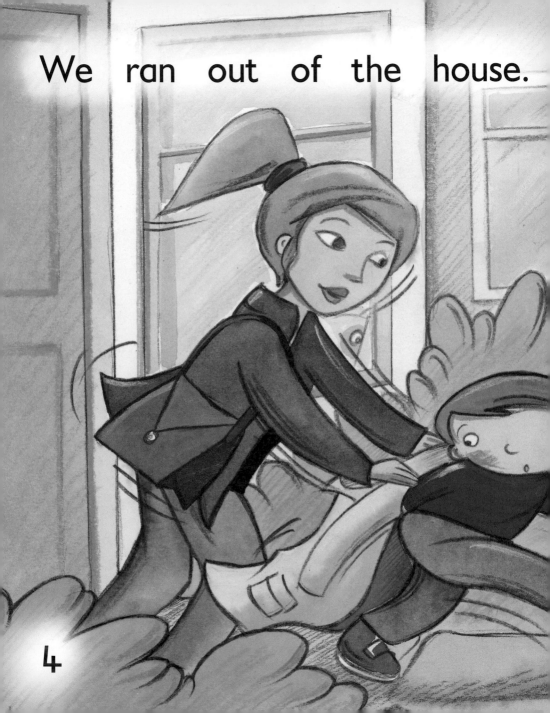

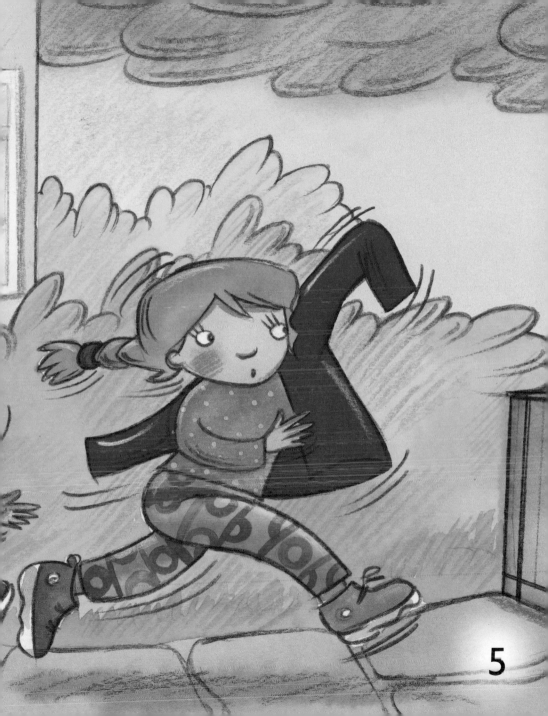

We ran to the shops.

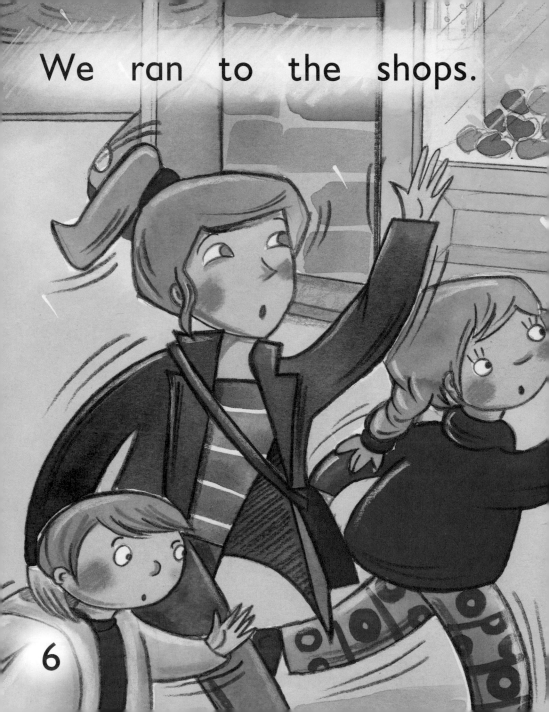

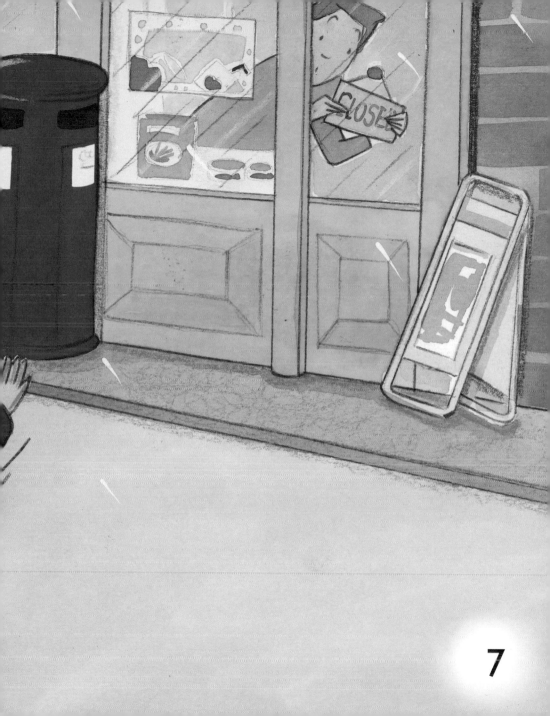

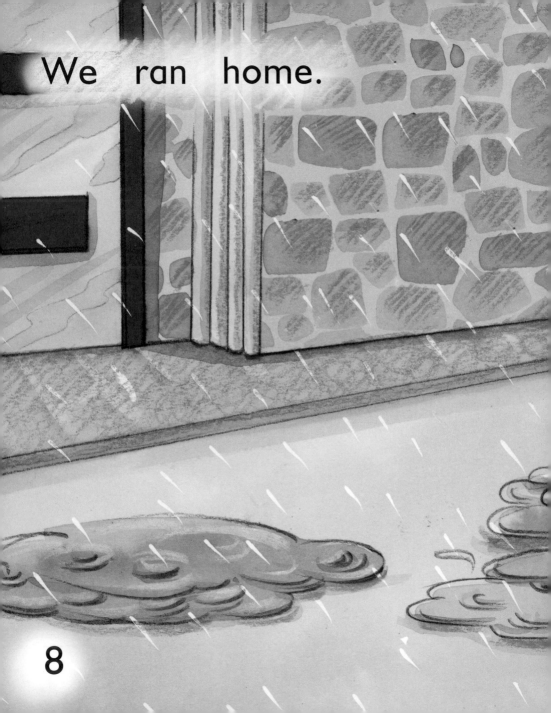

We ran home.

8

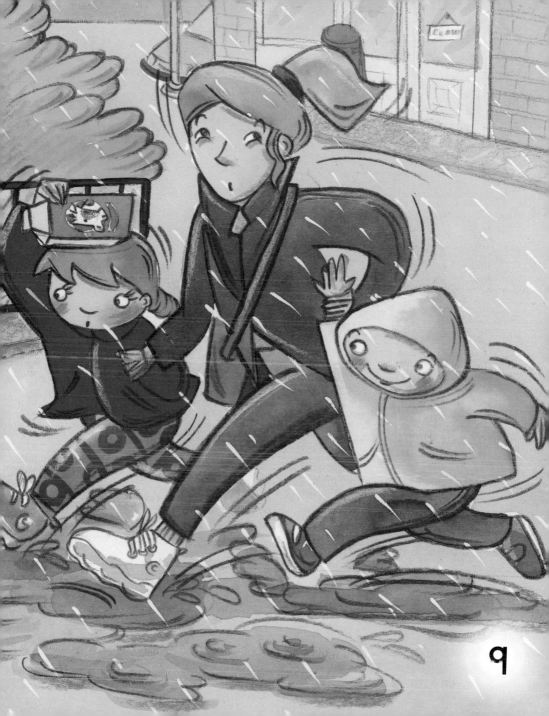

We ran upstairs.

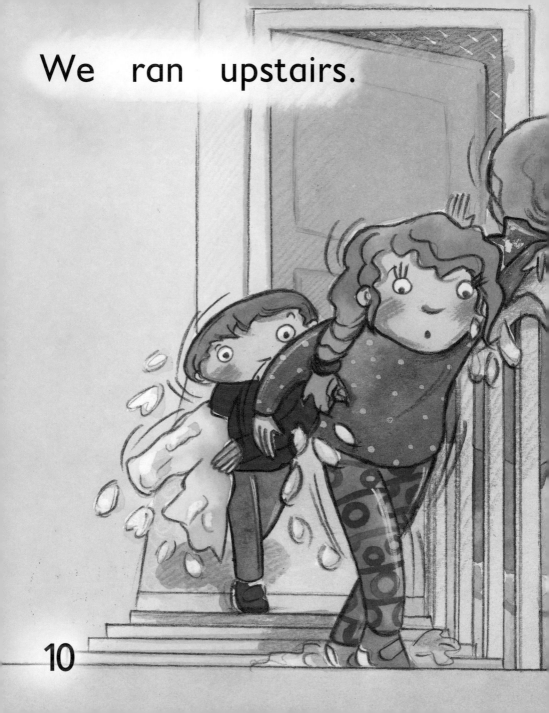

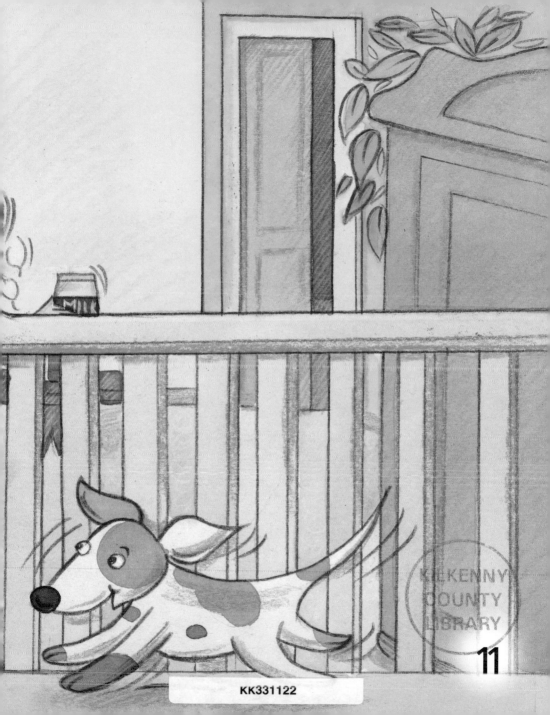

11

We ran a bath.

12

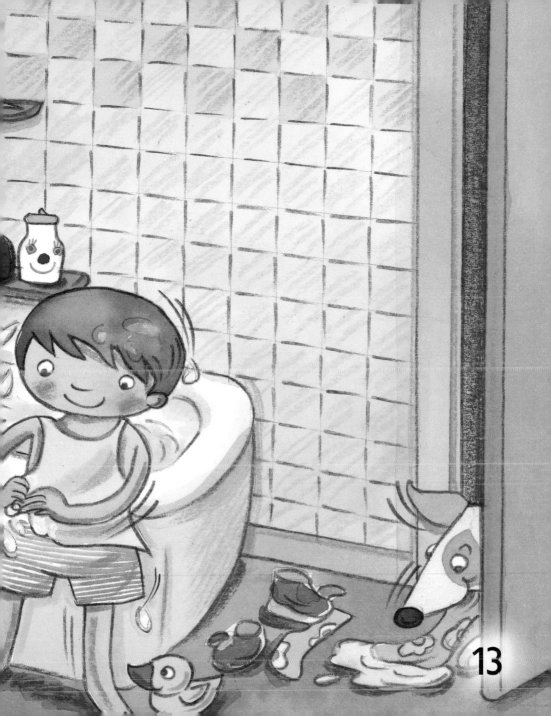

13

We ran downstairs.

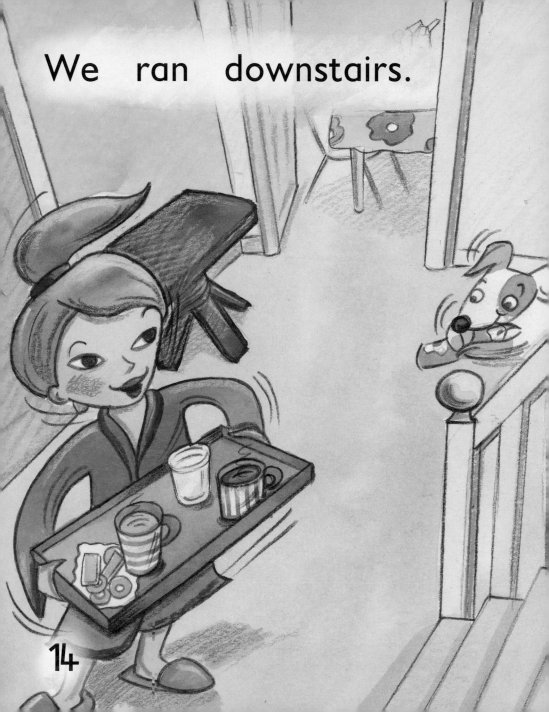

14

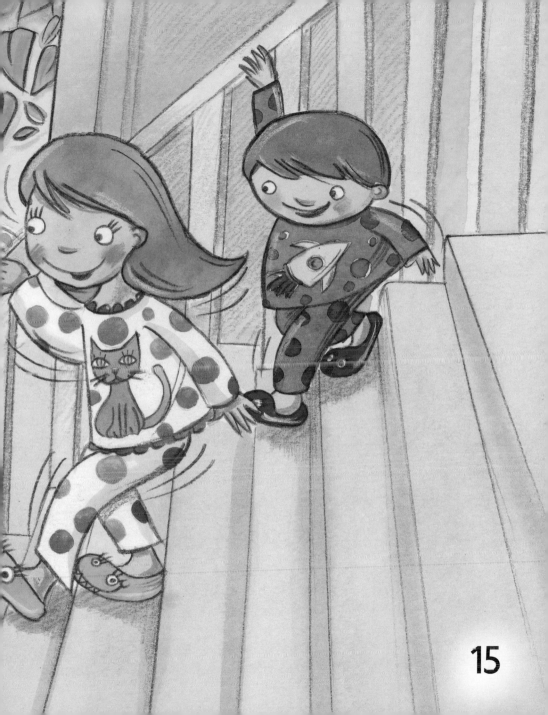

15

We ran out of milk again!

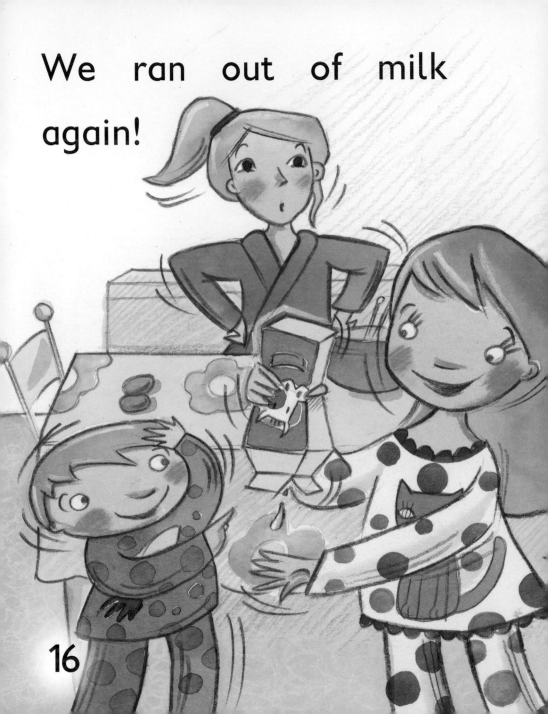

16